Mr. Clown's Directions

Draw a nose on the clown and color it red.
Draw three square buttons on the clown's shirt.
Draw a hat on the clown and color it yellow.
Draw a box of popcorn in the clown's hand.
Color the seals black.

Left to Right Magicians

Trace each line.

Tracing from left to right

Top to Bottom Beanstalks

Trace each line.

Mother Hubbard's Paths

Trace each line.

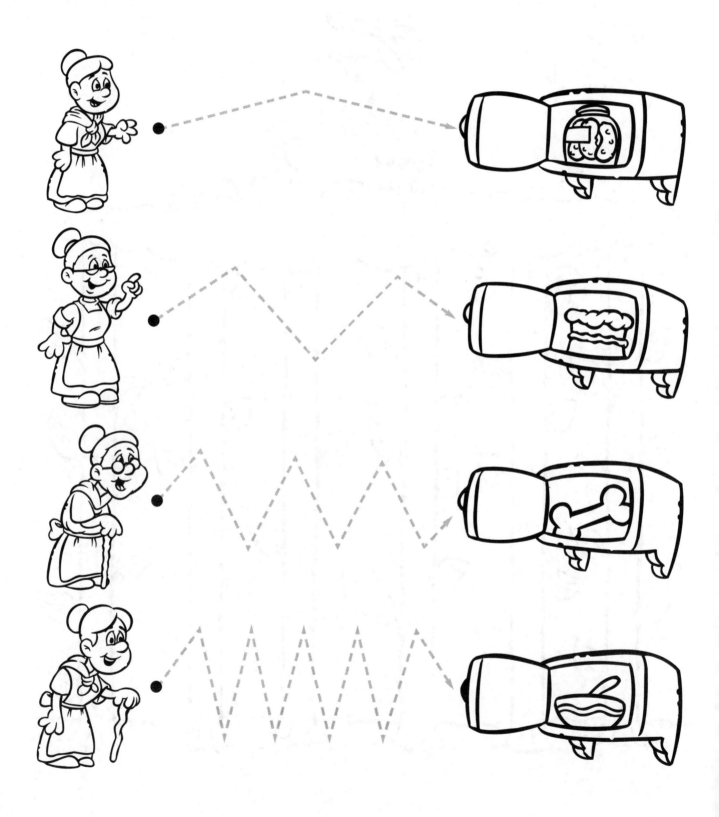

Tracing from left to right

Hickory Dickory Dock

Draw the path to the cheese.

Hey Diddle Diddle

Draw the path to the spoon.

Developing fine motor control; drawing a path to complete a maze

Circus Tricks

Color the one that is different.

Sea Creatures

Color the one that faces a different way.

Recognizing differences in direction

Pack Your Bag

Color what belongs in the .

Weather Match Up

Match the pictures that go together.

Recognizing pictures that go together

What Goes Together?

Color the pictures that go together the same color.

Does It Belong?

Circle the picture that does not belong. Color the others.

Classifying objects; recognizing objects that do not belong

What Doesn't Belong?

Color the picture that does not belong.

Mouse's warm mitten

Circle **M** and **m** above.
Color the pictures that begin with the **Mm** sound to make a path to the cheese.

Trace and write the letters.

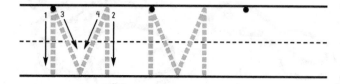

Identifying the letter **Mm** and its sound; tracing and printing **Mm**

Tommy's Turtle telephone

Circle **T** and **t** above.
Color the pictures that begin with the **Tt** sound.

Trace and write the letters.

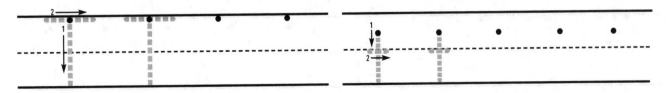

Frank's fishy faucet

Circle **F** and **f** above.
Color the spaces with pictures
that begin with the **Ff** sound.

Ff

Trace and write the letters.

Identifying the letter **Ff** and its sound; tracing and printing **Ff**

Henry Hippo's horn

Circle **H** and **h** above.
Draw a line from **Hh** to each picture
that begins with the **Hh** sound.

Trace and write the letters.

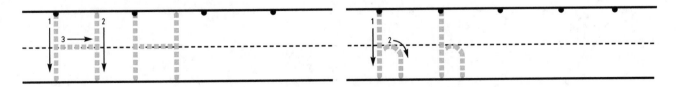

Nurse Nancy's news

Circle **N** and **n** above.
Draw a line from the nurse to each picture that
begins with the **Nn** sound.

Nn

Trace and write the letters.

Identifying the letter **Nn** and its sound; tracing and printing **Nn**

Astronaut Ann's apple

Circle **A** and **a** above.
Color the pictures that begin with the **Aa** sound.

Aa

Trace and write the letters.

Bobby Bear's balloons

Circle **B** and **b** above.
Color the balloons with objects
that begin with the **Bb** sound.

Trace and write the letters.

Identifying the letter **Bb** and its sound; tracing and printing **Bb**

Patty Pig's puppet

Circle **P** and **p** above.
Draw a line from **Pp** to the pictures
that begin with the **Pp** sound.

Trace and write the letters.

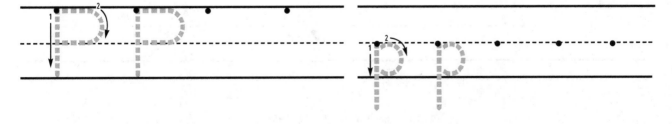

Sammy Seal loves the sun

Circle **S** and **s** above.
Circle the pictures that begin with the **Ss** sound.
Color the seal.

Trace and write the letters.

Identifying the letter **Ss** and its sound; tracing and printing **Ss**

Very nice valentine

Circle **V** and **v** above.
Color the pictures that begin with the **Vv** sound.

Vv

Trace and write the letters.

V V

v v

Eddie Elephant's egg

Circle **E** and **e** above.
Circle the picture in each box
that begins with the **Ee** sound.

Trace and write the letters.

 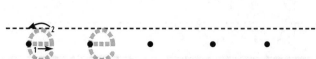

Identifying the letter **Ee** and its sound; tracing and printing **Ee**

Lucky Lion's living room

Circle **L** and **l** above.
Color the pictures that begin with the **Ll** sound.

Ll

Trace and write the letters.

Danny Dinosaur's dish

Circle **D** and **d** above.
Follow the pictures that begin with the **Dd** sound to draw a path from the dog to the doghouse.

Trace and write the letters.

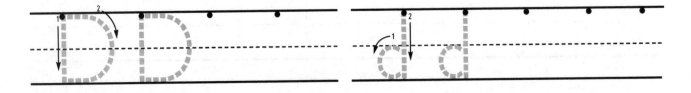

Identifying the letter **Dd** and its sound; tracing and printing **Dd**

Gabby Goose's garden gate

Circle **G** and **g** above.
Circle the pictures that begin with the **Gg** sound.

Trace and write the letters.

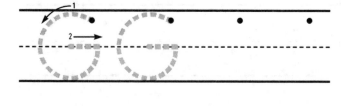 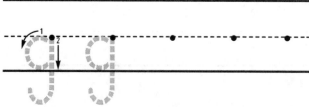

Carl Camel's cap

Circle **C** and **c** above.
Color the picture in each box
that begins with the **Cc** sound.

Trace and write the letters.

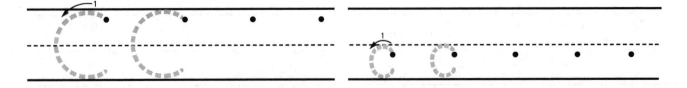

Identifying the letter **Cc** and its sound; tracing and printing **Cc**

Iggy Inchworm's igloo

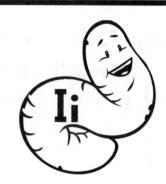

Circle **I** and **i** above.
Color the spaces with pictures
that begin with the **Ii** sound.

Trace and write the letters.

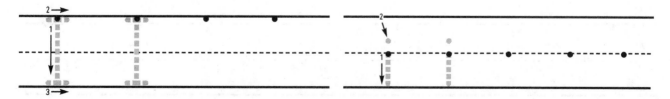

Ollie Octopus loves olives

Circle **O** and **o** above.
Circle the letter that stands for
each picture's beginning sound.

O   H

L   J

N   I

M   O

N   K

L   O

O   M

Trace and write the letters.

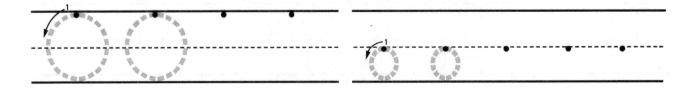

Identifying the letter **Oo** and its sound; tracing and printing **Oo**

Kipper Kangaroo's kite

Circle the letters **K** and **k** above.
Connect the ●s from **A** to **K**.
Connect the ■s from **a** to **k**.
Circle the picture in each kite that begins
with the **Kk** sound.

Trace and write the letters.

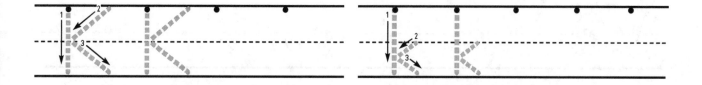

Wanda Witch's web

Circle **W** and **w** above.
Draw a line from the spider on the web to the
pictures that begin with the **Ww** sound.

Ww

Trace and write the letters.

Max's extra x-rays

Circle **X** and **x** above.
Draw a line to match each body part with its x-ray.

 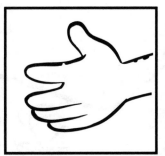 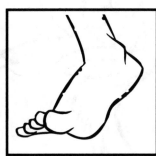 

 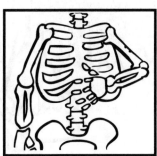  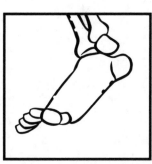

Trace and write the letters.

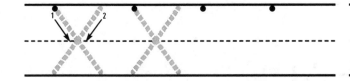 

Yellow Yak in the yard

Circle **Y** and **y** above.
Circle the pictures that begin with the **Yy** sound.
Color the yak yellow.

Trace and write the letters.

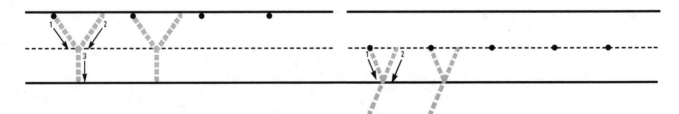

Identifying the letter **Yy** and its sound; tracing and printing **Yy**

Robot Rick's rocket

Circle **R** and **r** above.
Color the robot red.
Circle each picture in the rocket
that begins with the **Rr** sound.

Trace and write the letters.

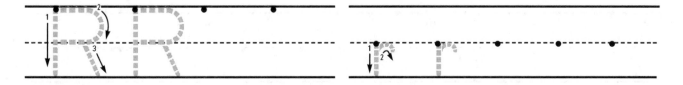

John's jar of jacks

Circle **J** and **j** above.
Cross out each picture that does not
begin with the **Jj** sound.

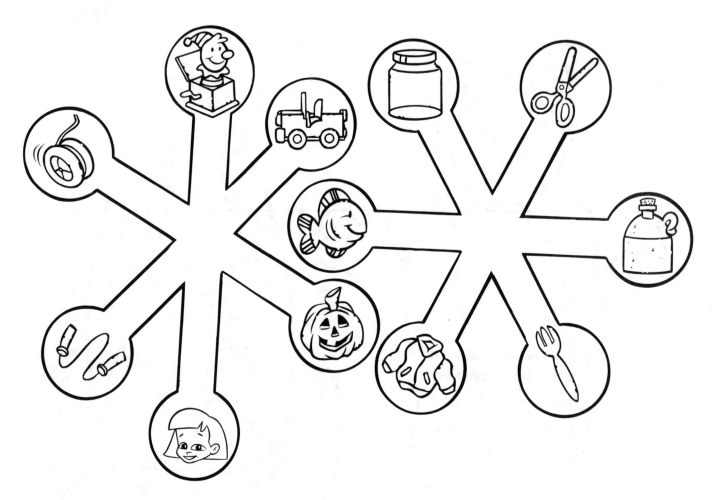

Trace and write the letters.

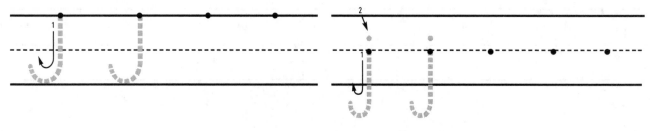

Identifying the letter **Jj** and its sound; tracing and printing **Jj**

Umpire under an umbrella

Circle **U** and **u** above.
Color the picture using the key.

Color Key
Color **R** green   Color **S** blue
Color **T** brown   Color **U** yellow

Trace and write the letters.

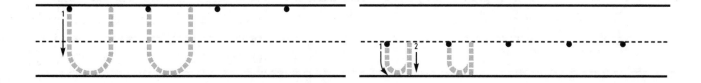

The Queen's quilt

Circle **Q** and **q** above.
Circle the pictures that begin with the **Qq** sound.
Connect the dots from **A** to **Q**.

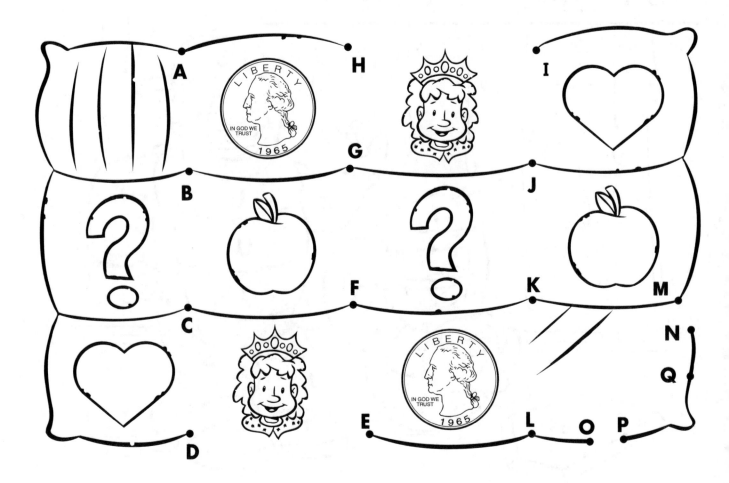

Trace and write the letters.

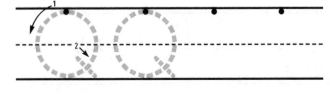

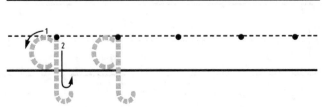

Identifying the letter **Qq** and its sound; tracing and printing **Qq**

Zebra zips to the zoo

Circle **Z** and **z** above.
Follow the letters from **Aa** to **Zz** to draw
a path from the zebra to the zoo.

Zz

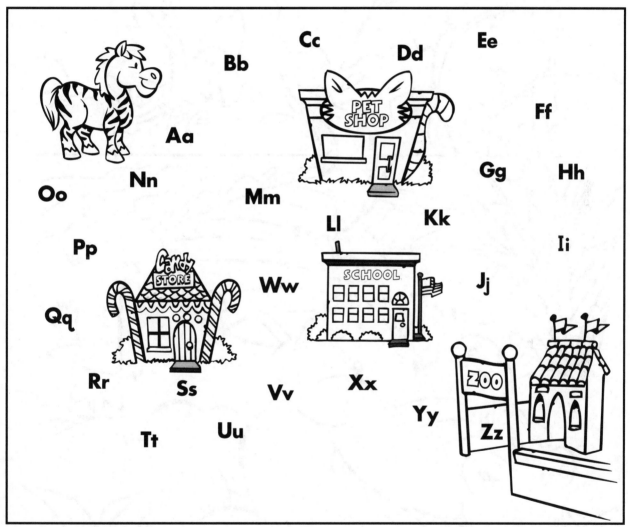

Trace and write the letters.

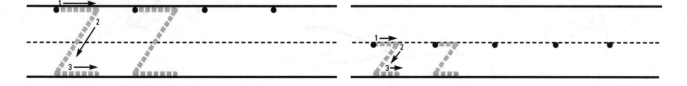

What's Hiding in the Swamp?

Connect the dots from **A** to **Z**.
Color the picture.

Developing fine motor control; practicing alphabetical order

What's My Sound?

Circle the letter that stands for each picture's beginning sound.

b f d	c s t	h d b
w v j	q j p	c v j
r g l	r q i	u y k
o m d	f w a	w v j

Time to Hear a Rhyme

Color the first picture in each row.
Circle the ones that rhyme with that picture.

Identifying pictures that rhyme

What's My Rhyme?

Color the first picture in each row.
Circle the ones that rhyme with that picture.

Clowning Around with Colors

Color the clown using the code.

r = red   **o** = orange   **y** = yellow

b = blue   **g** = green

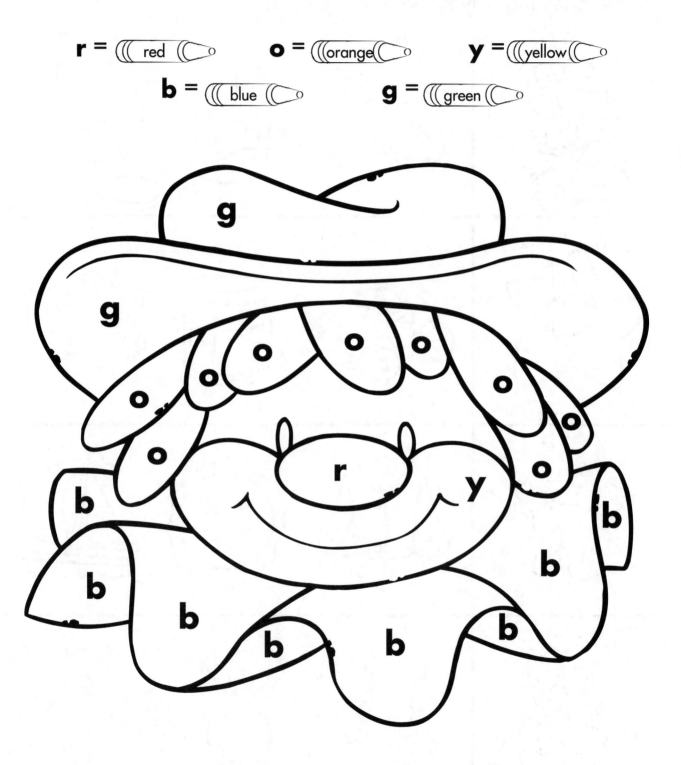

Identifying color words; following directions

Colorful Sea Creatures

Color the 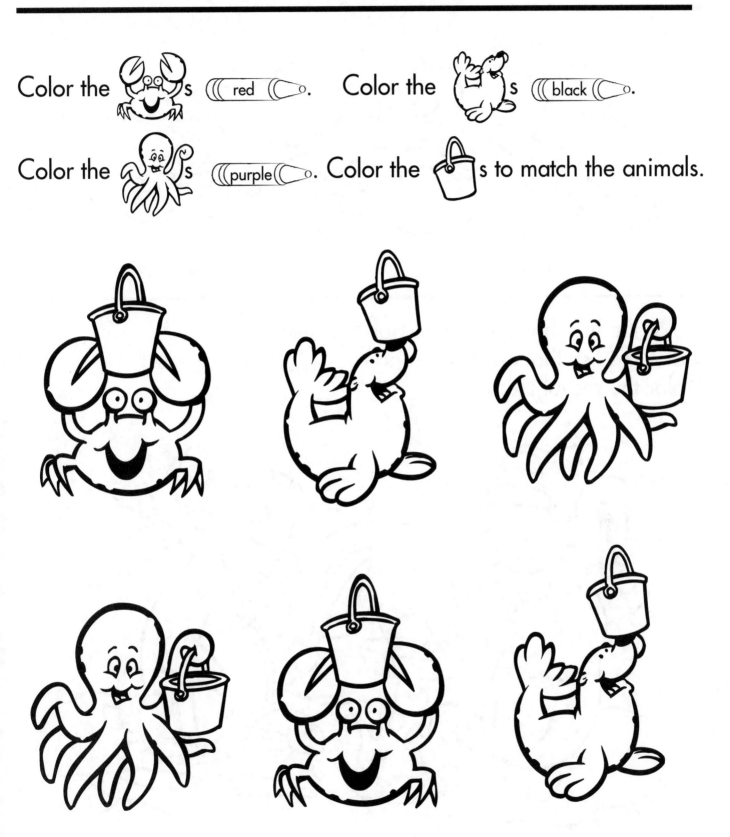s red. Color the s black.

Color the s purple. Color the s to match the animals.

On and Off

on   **off**

Color the fish that are **on** the pan ((purple)) .
Color the fish that are **off** the pan ((orange)) .
Color the rest of the picture.

Understanding opposites: **on** and **off**

Left and Right

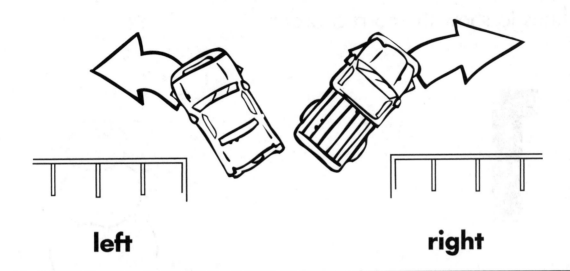

left   **right**

Color the object in the policeman's **left** hand red.
Color the object in the policemen's **right** hand green.
Color the rest of the picture.

Build a Snowman

Draw lines to show the correct order.

Recognizing the order of events

Puppy Love

Write **1**, **2**, and **3** to show
the order of what happened.

Who is in the Cave?

Circle the word that is the same in each row.

we	**is**	(**we**)
go	**go**	**am**
in	**to**	**in**
it	**it**	**do**

Identifying words that are the same; introducing sight words

Ship Ahoy!

Trace the lines. Color the picture.

Follow the Logs

Draw the path to the dam.

Review drawing a path to complete a maze

Flying High

Color the one that faces a different way.

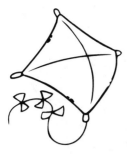   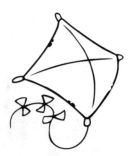

Who Lives on a Farm?

Color the .
Then color all the things that live on a farm.

Pick the Partner

Match the capital and lowercase letter partners.

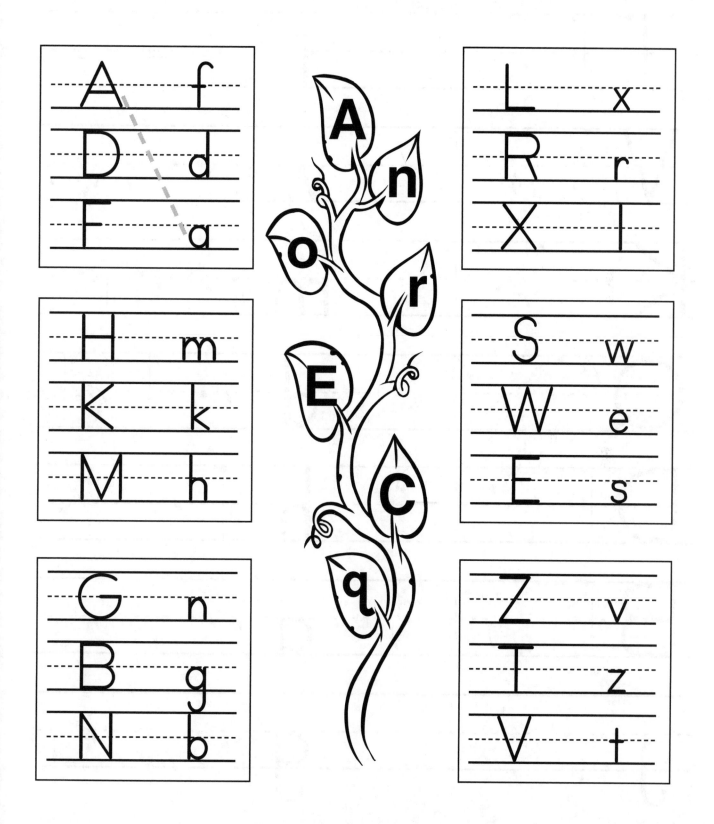

Write it Right!

Trace.

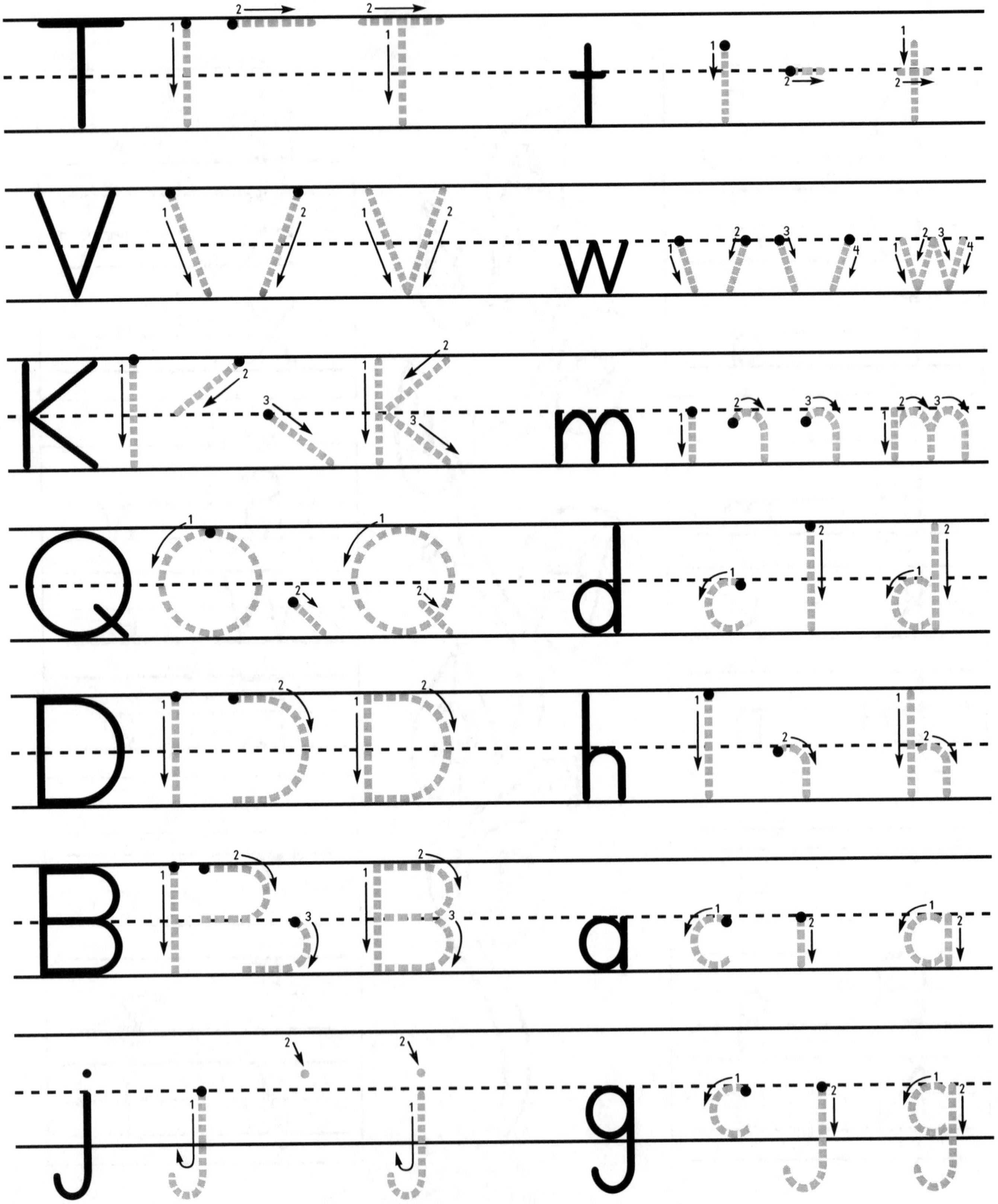

T T T t t i i t

V V V w w w w

K K K m m m

Q Q Q d d d

D D D h h h

B B B a c a

j j j g c j g

Review letter formations

Same Sound

Match the pictures that begin with the same sound.

On-the-Go Rhymes

Match the ones that rhyme.

Reviewing pictures that rhyme

Color My World

Color the  yellow.

Color the orange.

Color the blue.

Color the purple.

Color the red.

Mixed-up Stories

Circle **1**, **2**, or **3** to show the order.

1   **2**   **3**

1   **2**   **3**

1   **2**   **3**

1   **2**   **3**

1   **2**   **3**

1   **2**   **3**

Reviewing the order of events

Answer Key

Please take time to review the work your child has completed and remember to praise both success and effort. If your child makes a mistake, let him or her know that mistakes are a part of learning. Then explain the correct answer and how to find it. Taking the time to help your child and an active interest in his or her progress shows that you feel learning is important.

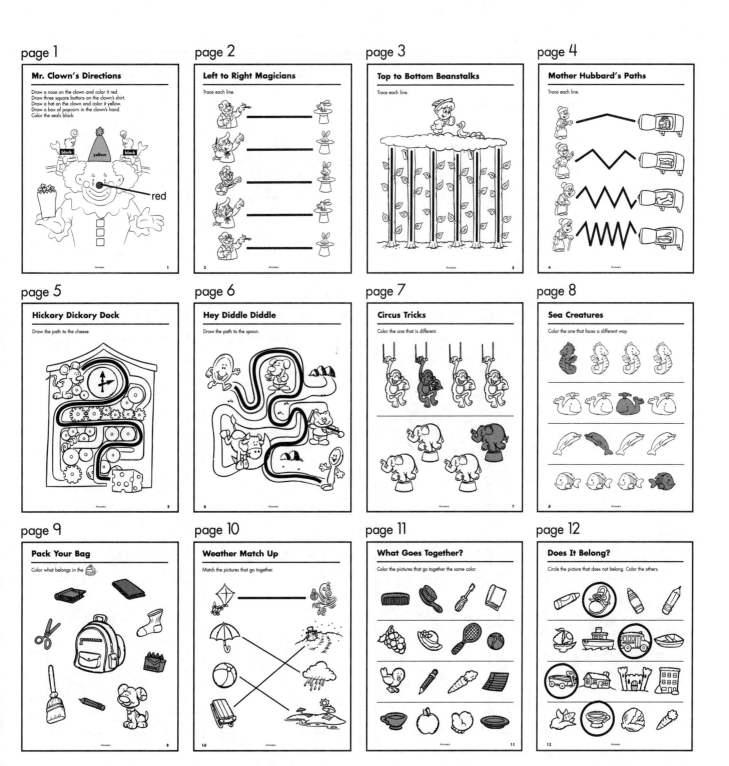

What Doesn't Belong?

Color the picture that does not belong.

Mouse's warm mitten

Circle **M** and **m** above.
Color the pictures that begin with the **Mm** sound to make a path to the cheese.

Trace and write the letters.

Tommy's Turtle telephone

Circle **T** and **t** above.
Color the pictures that begin with the **Tt** sound.

Trace and write the letters.

Frank's fishy faucet

Circle **F** and **f** above.
Color the spaces with pictures that begin with the **Ff** sound.

Trace and write the letters.

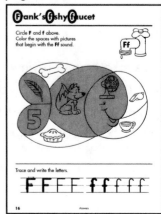

Henry Hippo's horn

Circle **H** and **h** above.
Draw a line from **Hh** to each picture that begins with the **Hh** sound.

Trace and write the letters.

Nurse Nancy's news

Circle **N** and **n** above.
Draw a line from the nurse to each picture that begins with the **Nn** sound.

Trace and write the letters.

Astronaut Ann's apple

Circle **A** and **a** above.
Color the pictures that begin with the **Aa** sound.

Trace and write the letters.

Baby Bear's balloons

Circle **B** and **b** above.
Color the balloons with objects that begin with the **Bb** sound.

Trace and write the letters.

Patty Pig's puppet

Circle **P** and **p** above.
Draw a line from **Pp** to the pictures that begin with the **Pp** sound.

Trace and write the letters.

Sammy Seal loves the sun

Circle **S** and **s** above.
Circle the pictures that begin with the **Ss** sound.
Color the seal.

Trace and write the letters.

Very nice valentine

Circle **V** and **v** above.
Color the pictures that begin with the **Vv** sound.

Trace and write the letters.

Eddie Elephant's egg

Circle **E** and **e** above.
Circle the picture in each box that begins with the **Ee** sound.

Trace and write the letters.

Lucky Lion's living room

Circle **L** and **l** above.
Color the pictures that begin with the **Ll** sound.

Trace and write the letters.

Danny Dinosaur's dish

Circle **D** and **d** above.
Follow the pictures that begin with the **Dd** sound to draw a path from the dog to the doghouse.

Trace and write the letters.

Gabby Goose's garden gate

Circle **G** and **g** above.
Circle the pictures that begin with the **Gg** sound.

Trace and write the letters.

Carl Camel's cap

Circle **C** and **c** above.
Color the picture in each box that begins with the **Cc** sound.

Trace and write the letters.

page 29

Iggy Inchworm's igloo

Circle I and i above.
Color the spaces with pictures
that begin with the Ii sound.

Trace and write the letters.

I I I I   i i i i i

29

page 30

Olie Octopus loves Olives

Circle O and o above.
Circle the letter that stands for
each picture's beginning sound.

Trace and write the letters.

O O O O   o o o o o

30   Answers

page 31

Kipper Kangaroo's kite

Circle the letters K and k above.
Connect the es from A to K.
Connect the as from a to k.
Circle the picture in each kite that begins
with the Kk sound.

Trace and write the letters.

K K K K   k k k k k

Answers   31

page 32

Wanda Witch's web

Circle W and w above.
Draw a line from the spider on the web to the
pictures that begin with the Ww sound.

Trace and write the letters.

W W W   w w w

32   Answers

page 33

Max's extra x-rays

Circle X and x above.
Draw a line to match each body part with its x-ray.

Trace and write the letters.

X X X X   x x x x x

Answers   33

page 34

Yellow Yak in the yard

Circle Y and y above.
Circle the pictures that begin with the Yy sound.
Color the yak yellow.

Trace and write the letters.

Y Y Y Y   y y y y y

34   Answers

page 35

Robot Rick's rocket

Circle R and r above.
Color the robot red.
Circle each picture in the rocket
that begins with the Rr sound.

Trace and write the letters.

R R R R   r r r r r

Answers   35

page 36

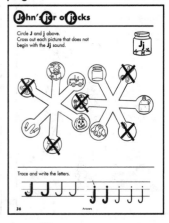

John's jar of jacks

Circle J and j above.
Cross out each picture that does not
begin with the Jj sound.

Trace and write the letters.

J J J J   j j j j j

36   Answers

page 37

Umpire under an umbrella

Circle U and u above.
Color the picture using the key.

Color Key
Color R (green)   Color S (blue)
Color T (brown)   Color U (yellow)

Trace and write the letters.

U U U U   u u u u u

Answers   37

page 38

The Queen's quilt

Circle Q and q above.
Circle the pictures that begin with the Qq sound.
Connect the dots from A to Q.

Trace and write the letters.

Q Q Q Q   q q q q q

38   Answers

page 39

Zebra zips to the zoo

Circle Z and z above.
Follow the letters from Aa to Zz to draw
a path from the zebra to the zoo.

Trace and write the letters.

Z Z Z Z   z z z z z

Answers   39

page 40

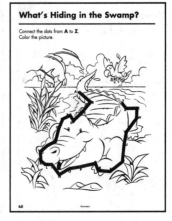

What's Hiding in the Swamp?

Connect the dots from A to Z.
Color the picture.

40   Answers

page 41

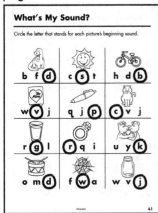

What's My Sound?

Circle the letter that stands for each picture's beginning sound.

b f (d)   c (s) t   h d (b)

w (v) j   q (p) p   c (v) j

r g (l)   (r) q i   u y (k)

o m (d)   f (w) a   w v (j)

41

page 42

Time to Hear a Rhyme

Color the first picture in each row.
Circle the ones that rhyme with that picture.

42   Answers

page 43

What's My Rhyme?

Color the first picture in each row.
Circle the ones that rhyme with that picture.

43

page 44

Clowning Around with Colors

Color the clown using the code.

r = red   o = orange   y = yellow
b = blue   g = green

44   Answers

Answers

63

page 45
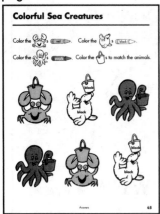
Colorful Sea Creatures

page 46

On and Off

on   off

page 47

Left and Right

left   right

page 48

Build a Snowman

Draw lines to show the correct order.

1
2
3

page 49

Puppy Love

Write 1, 2, and 3 to show the order of what happened.

page 50
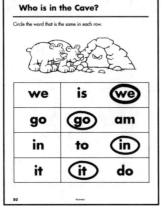
Who is in the Cave?

Circle the word that is the same in each row.

page 51

Ship Ahoy!

Trace the lines. Color the picture.

page 52

Follow the Logs

Draw the path to the dam.

page 53
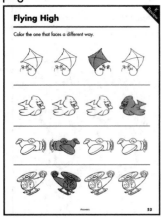
Flying High

Color the one that faces a different way.

page 54

Who Lives on a Farm?

Color the
Then color all the things that live on a farm.

page 55
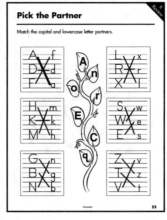
Pick the Partner

Match the capital and lowercase letter partners.

page 56
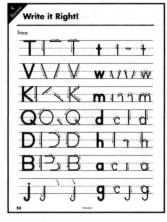
Write it Right!

Trace.

page 57
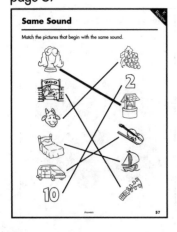
Same Sound

Match the pictures that begin with the same sound.

page 58
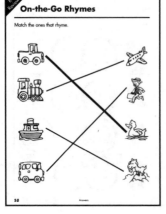
On-the-Go Rhymes

Match the ones that rhyme.

page 59

Color My World

Color the
Color the
Color the

page 60

Mixed-up Stories

Circle 1, 2, or 3 to show the order.